At the Seaside

Story by Neil Griffiths

Illustrated by Piers Harper

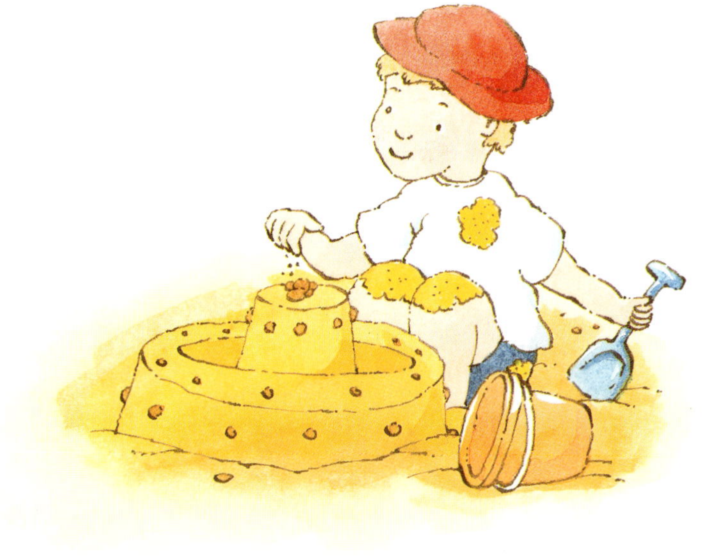

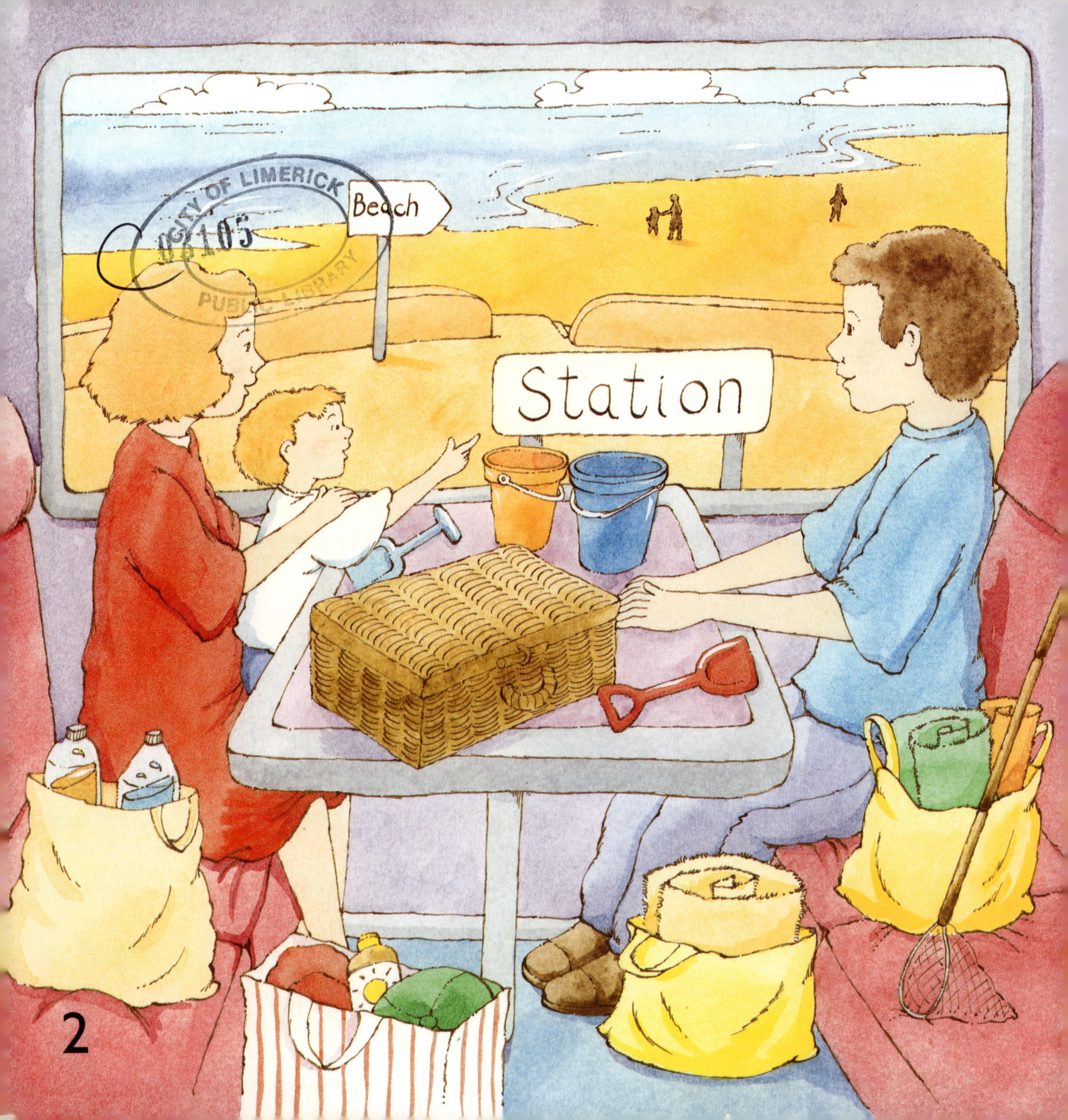
Beach
Station

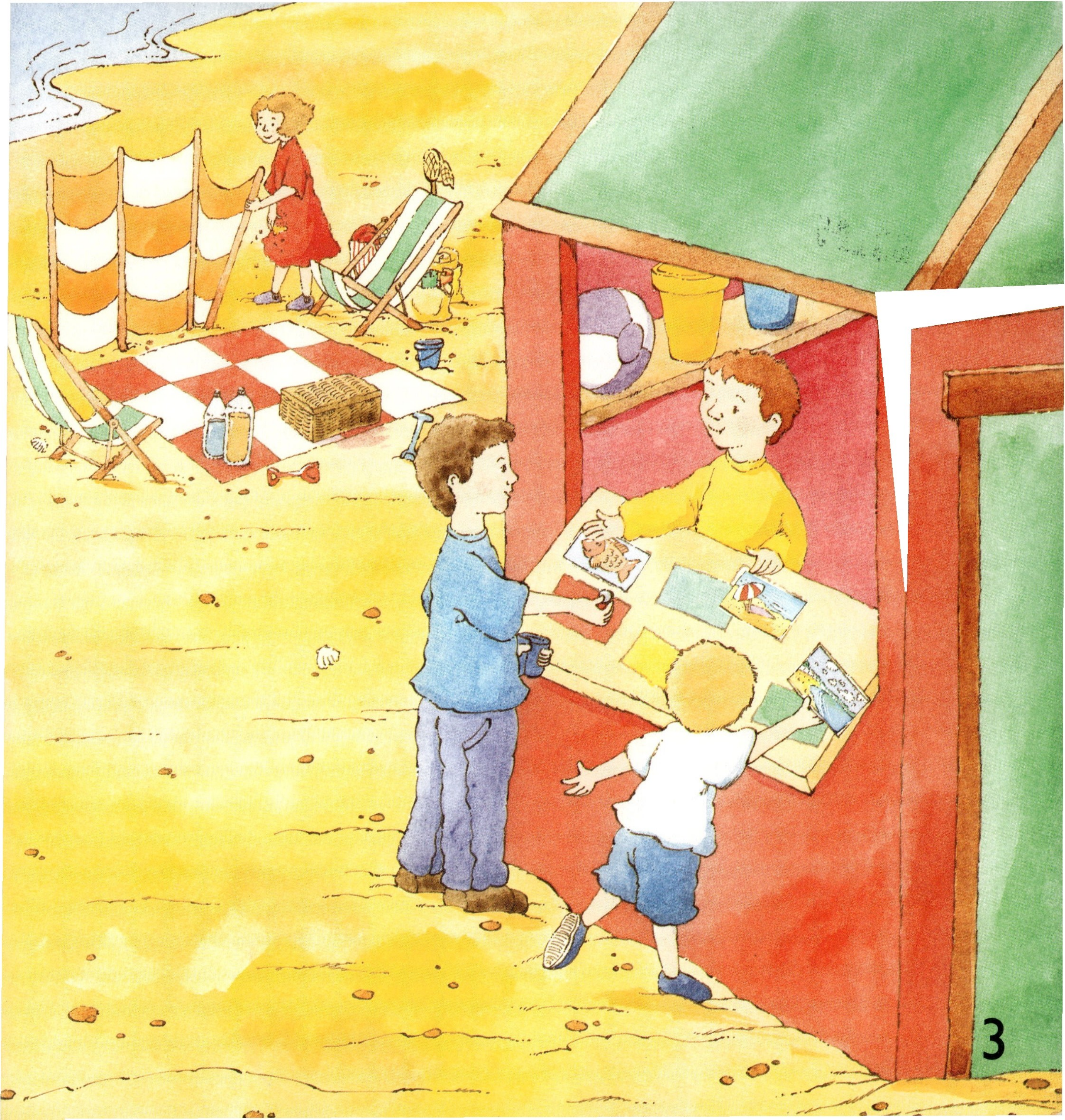

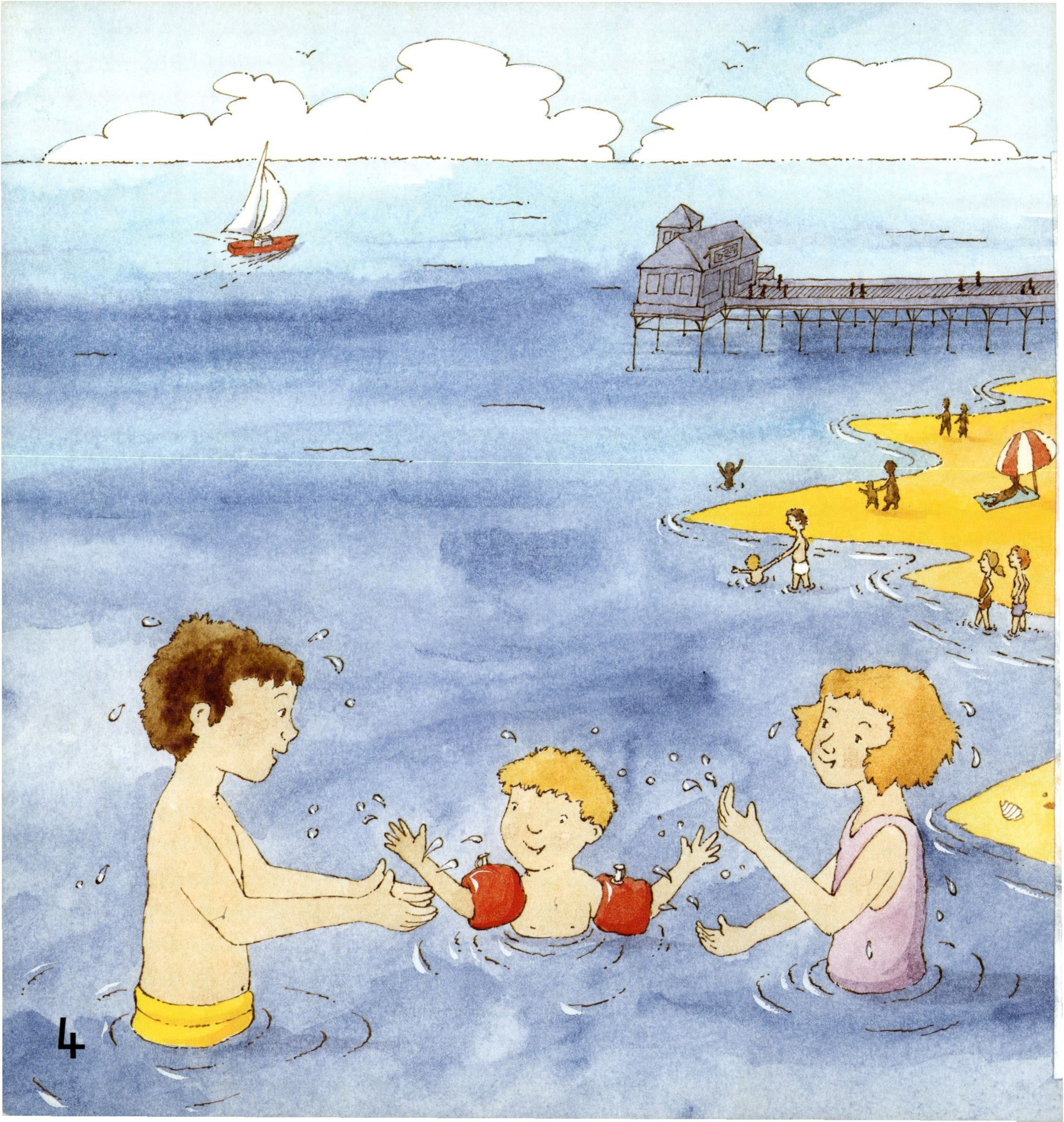

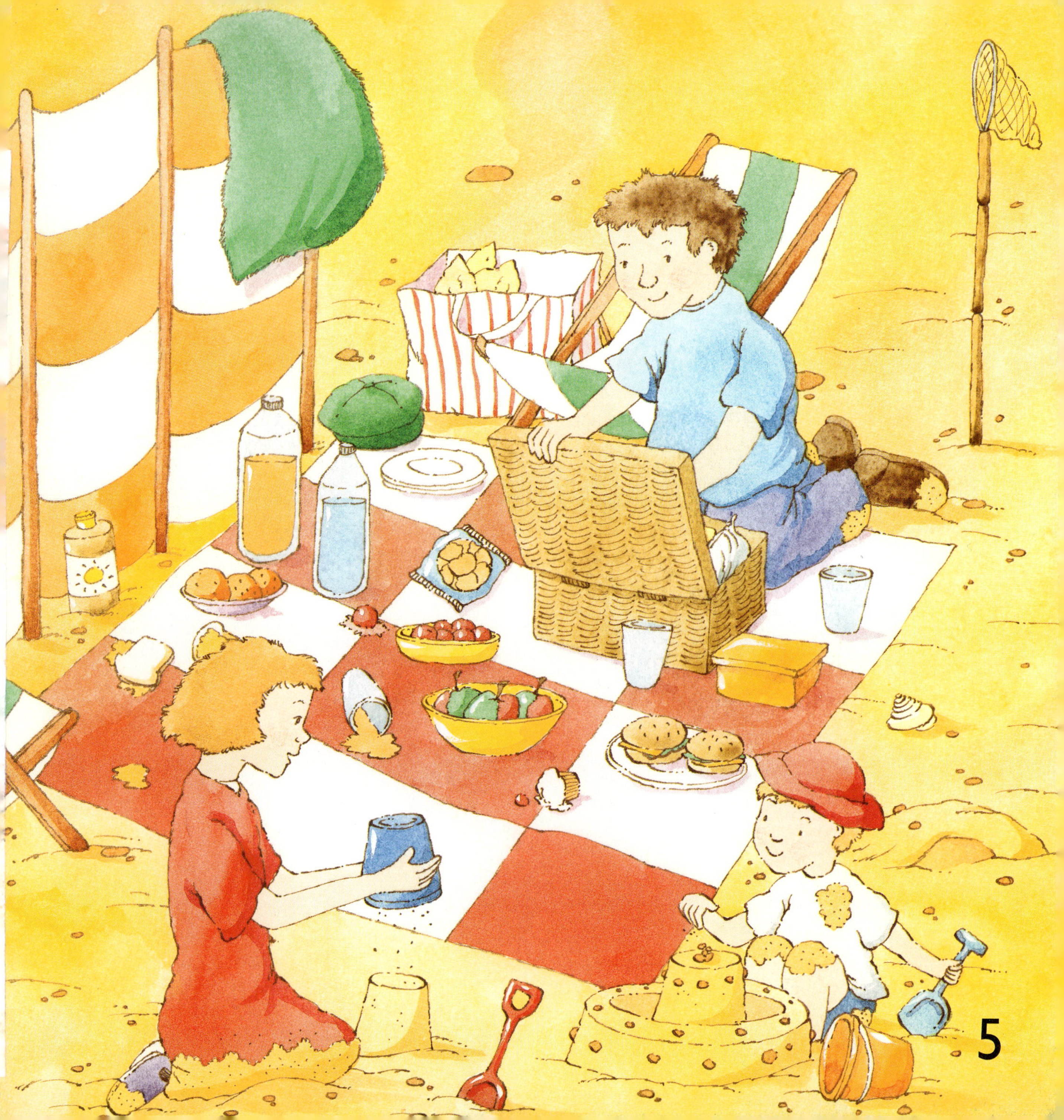

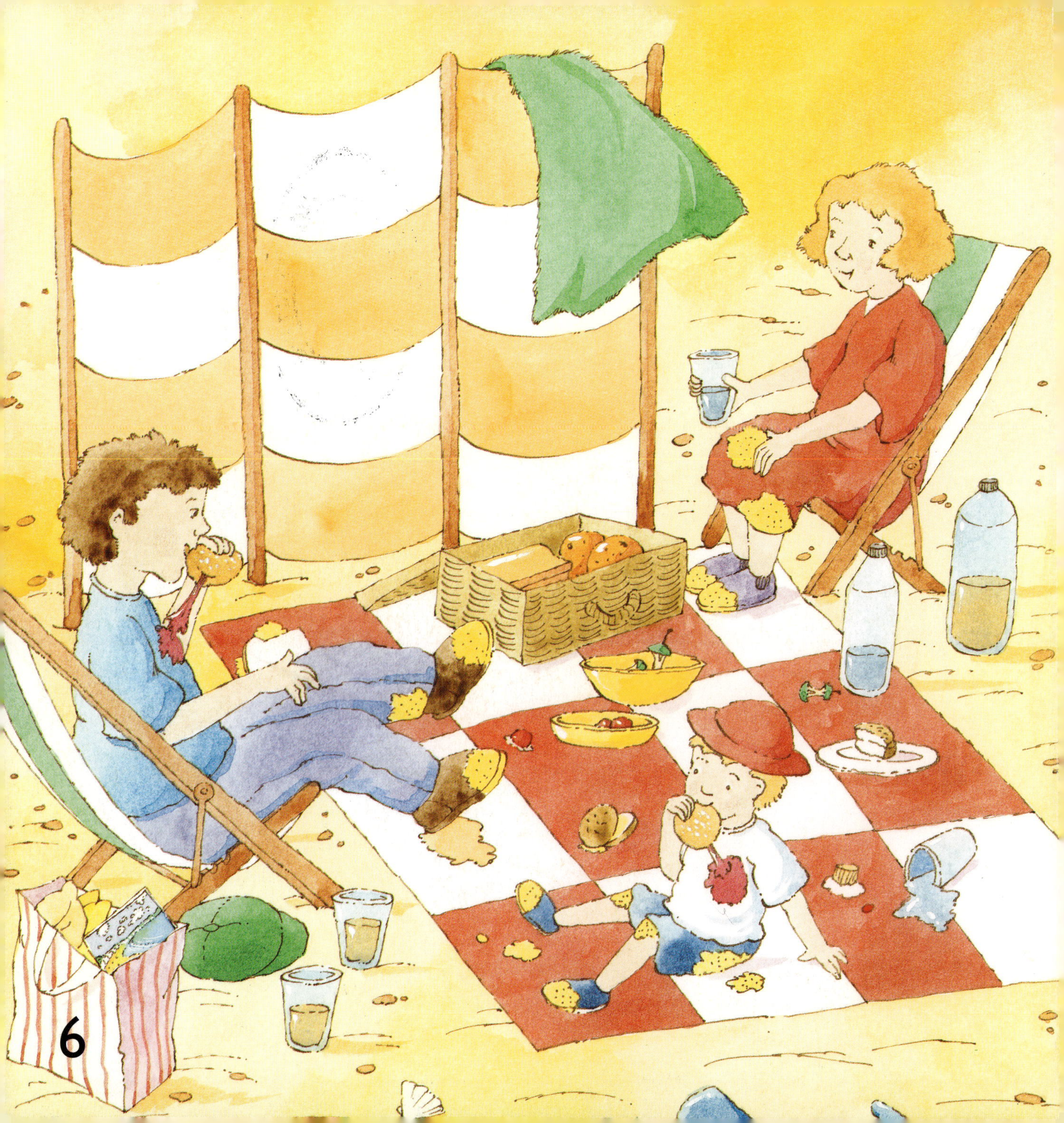

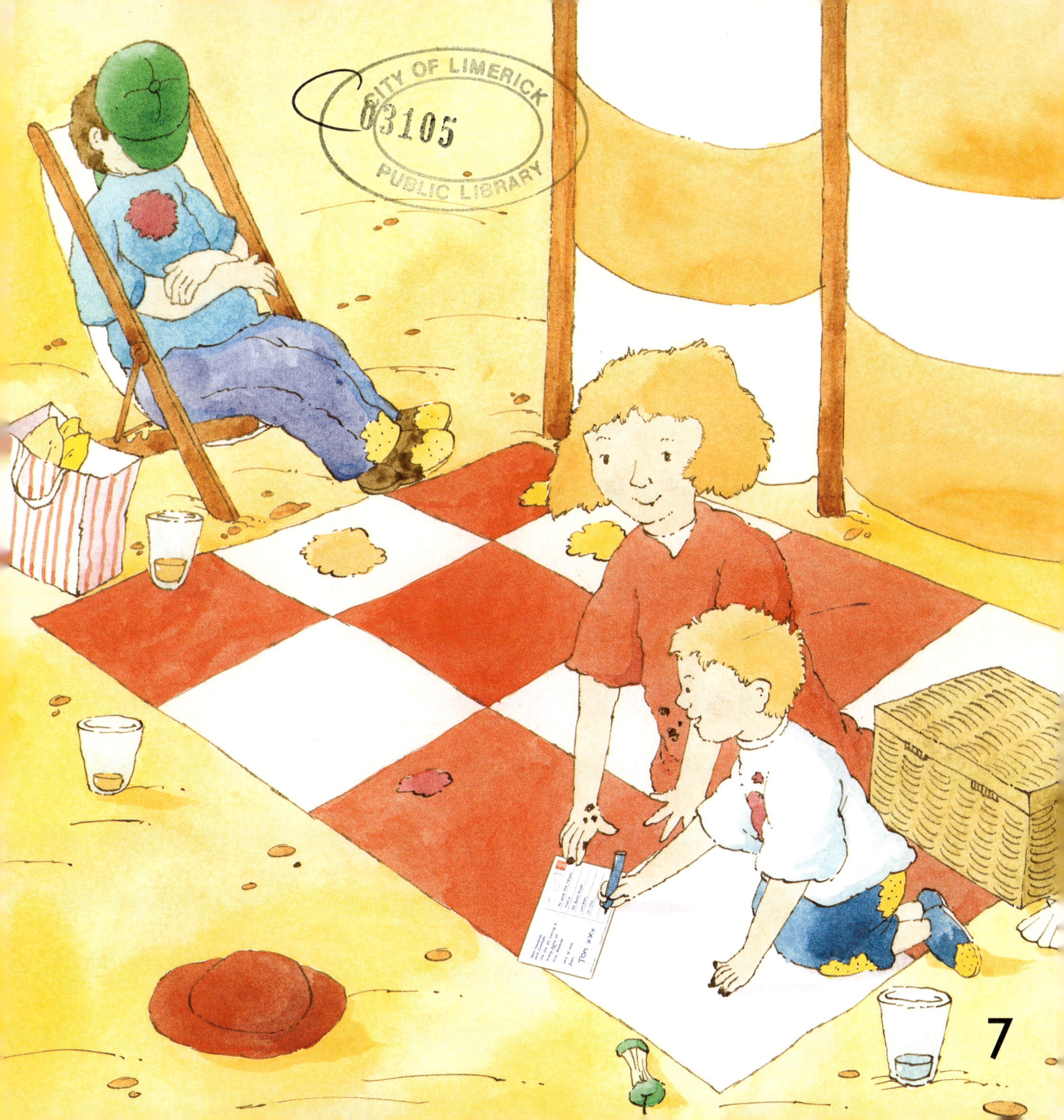
Tom xx

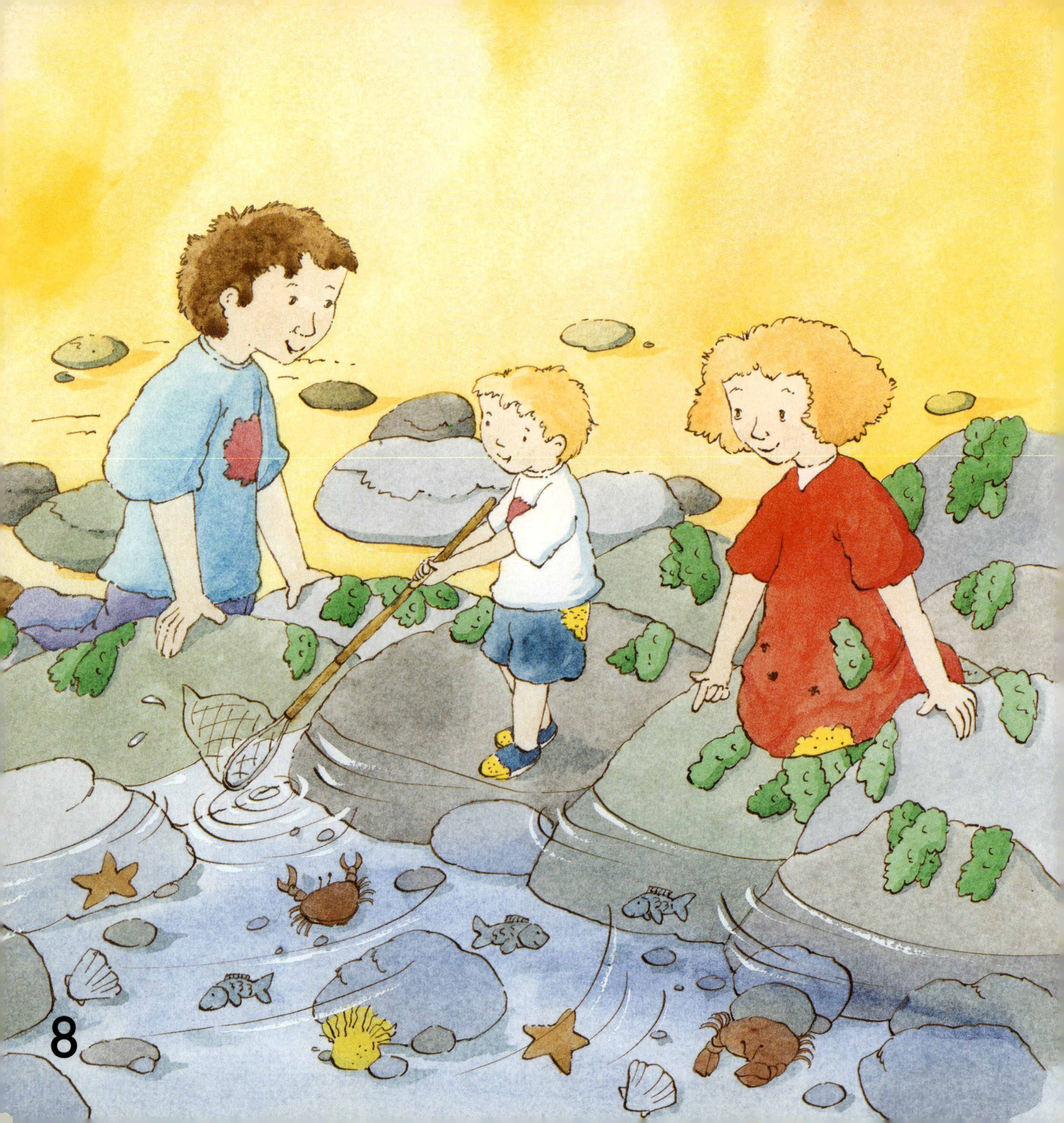

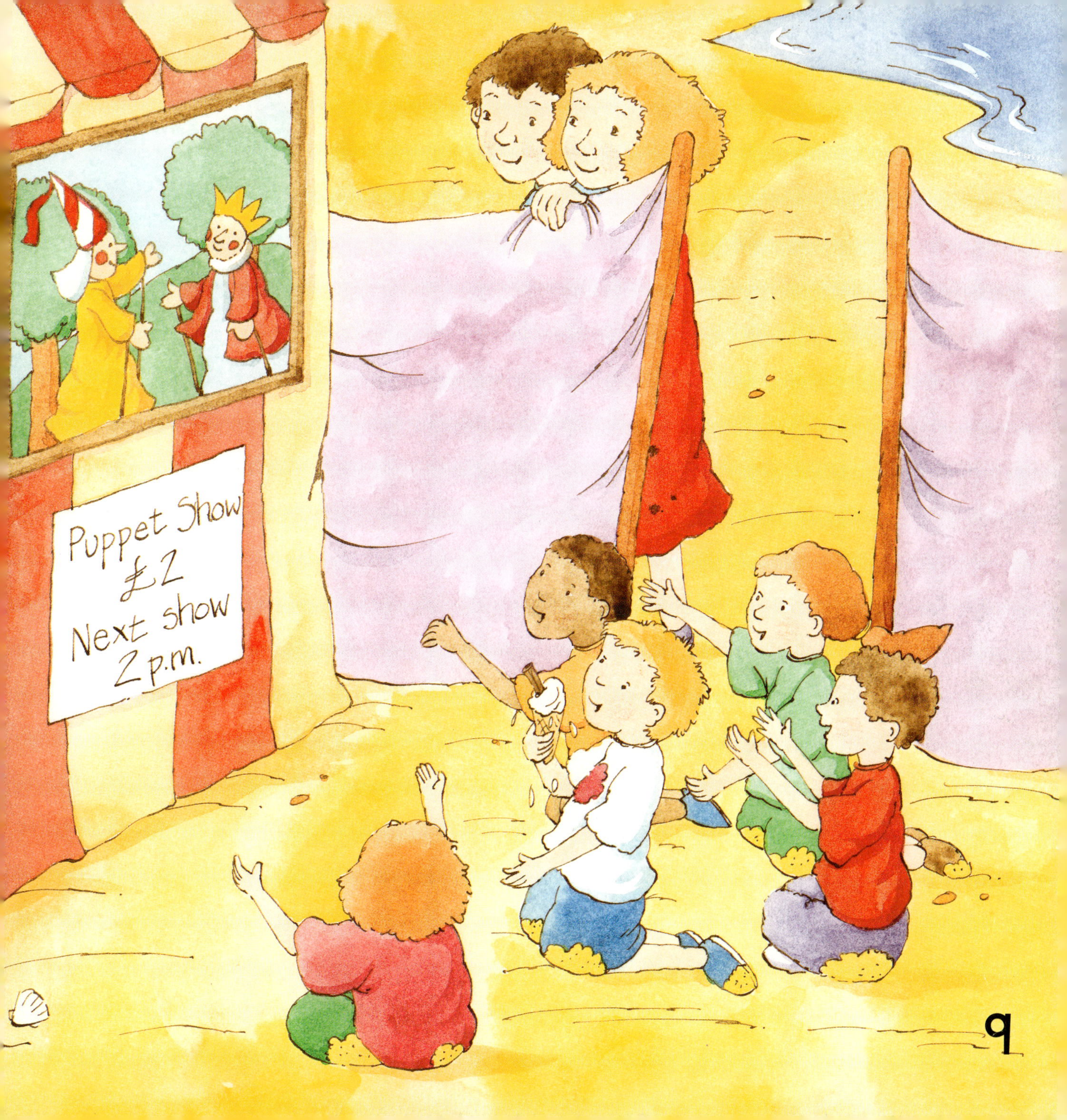
Puppet Show
£2
Next show
2 p.m.

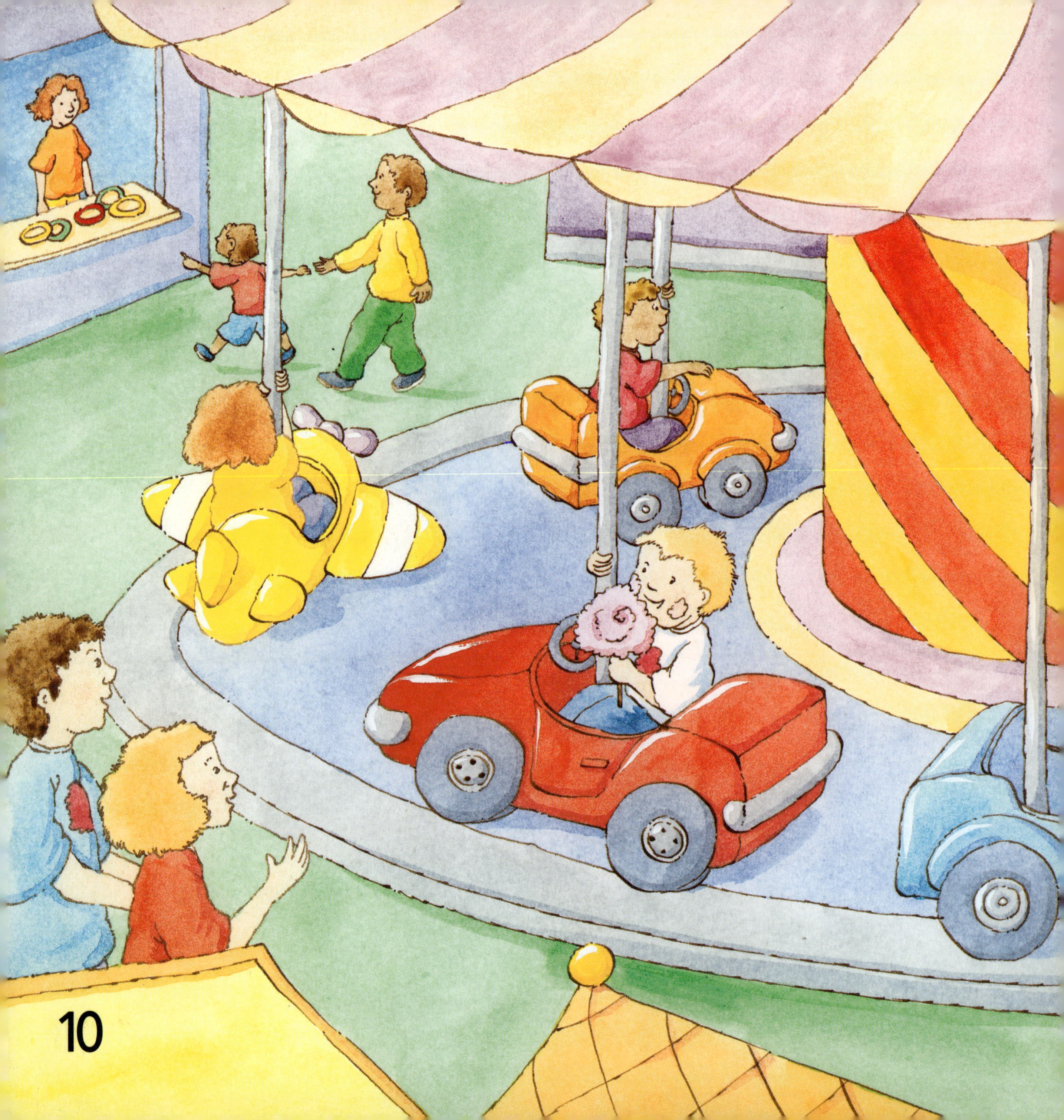

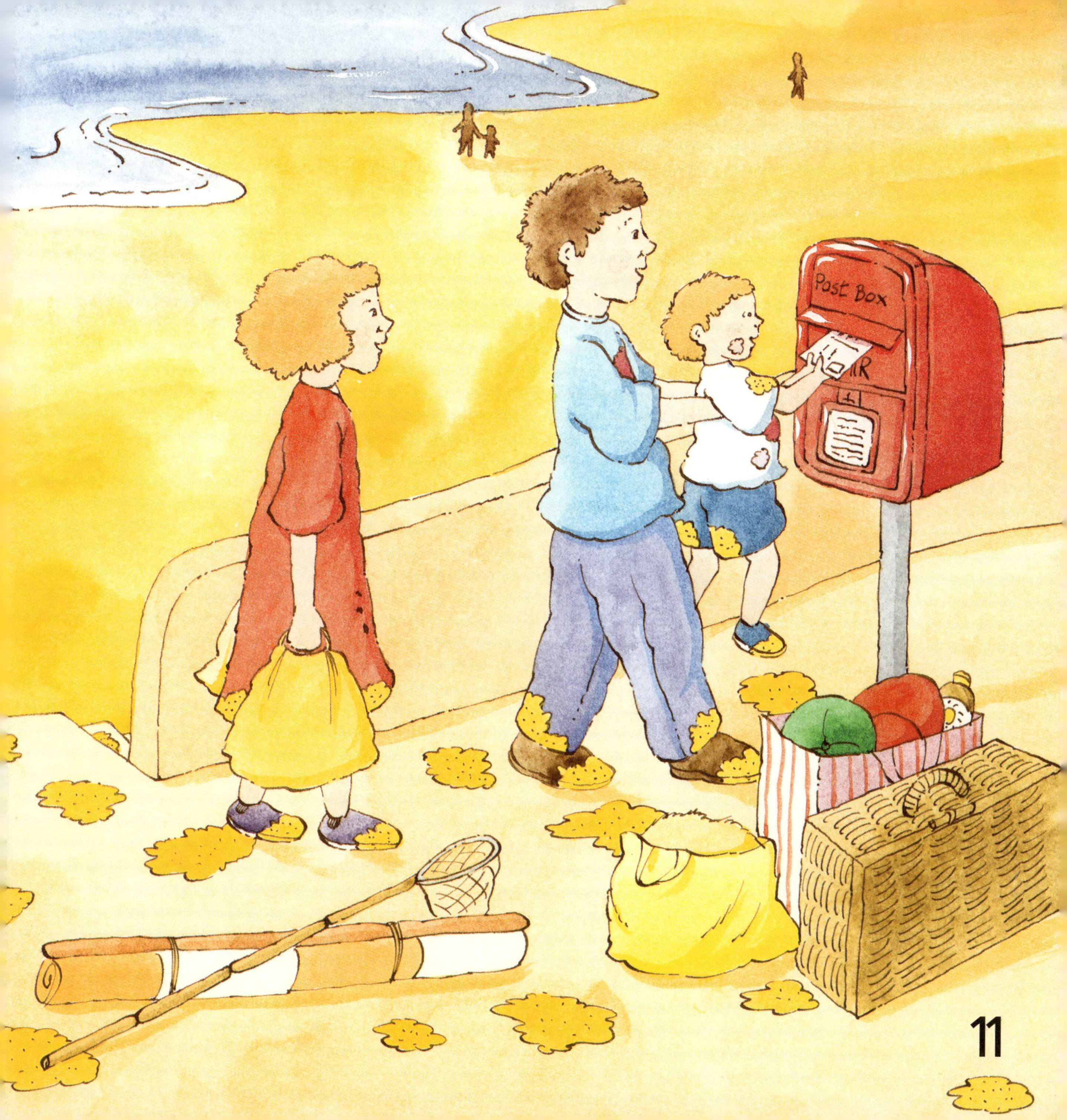
Post Box

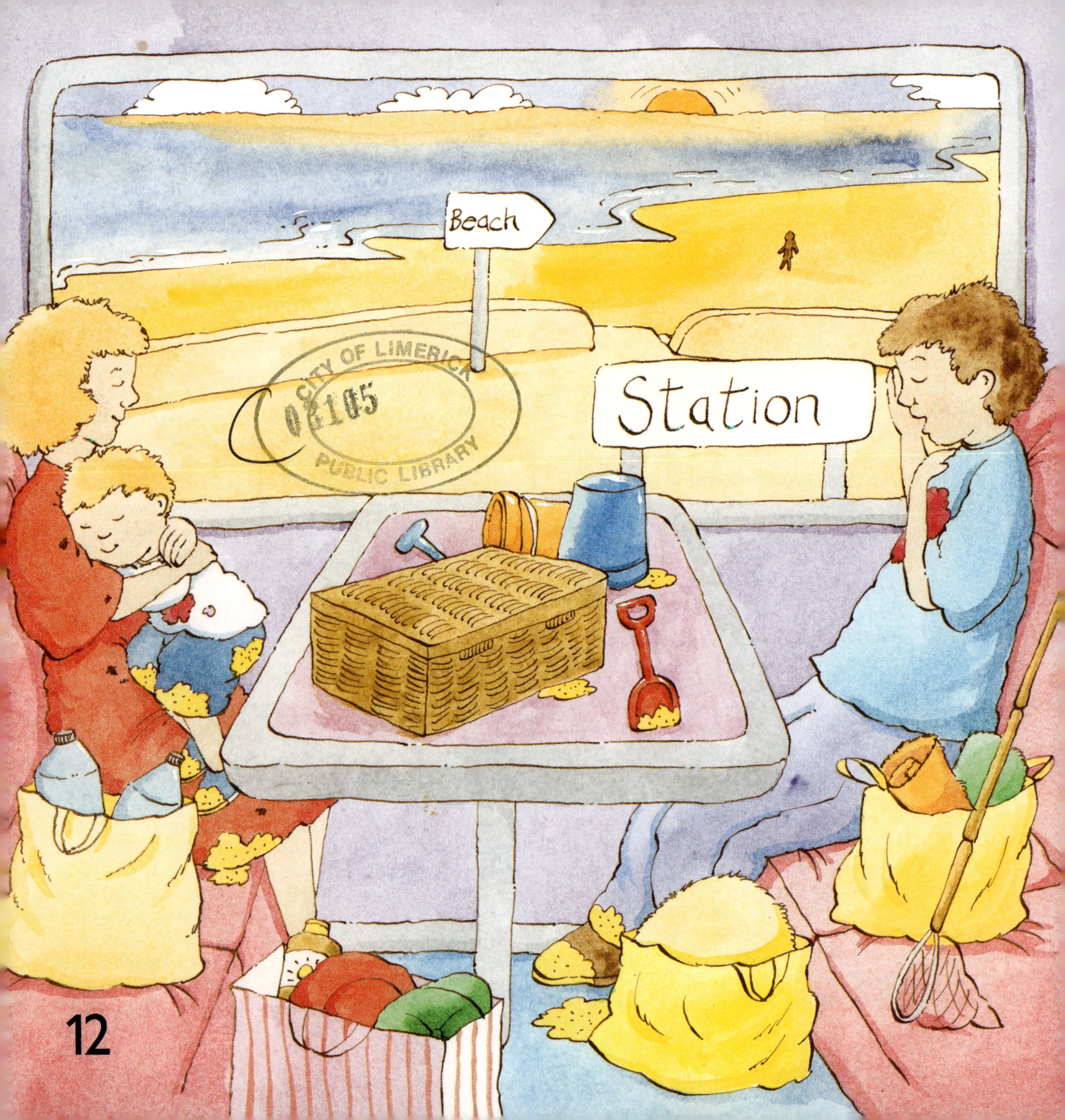
Beach
Station